Youth Asks,
Is God
A Game?

YOUTH FORUM SERIES

Titles in Print

YOUTH FORUM SERIES

Youth Asks, IS GOD A GAME?

by

Norman C. Habel

THOMAS NELSON INC.
CAMDEN, NEW JERSEY

Library of Congress Catalog Card Number: 76-110141

Foreword

Written in the context of the Christian faith, this book is one in a series published by Thomas Nelson Inc. in collaboration with Youth Research Center.

The research agency, which serves as editor of this series, is known through *What Youth Are Thinking* (Smedsrud, 1961) and *Profiles of Church Youth* (Strommen, 1963). The Director, Dr. Merton Strommen, is known also for his work as Director of Research (1965-67) with Religious Education Association, an inter-faith agency serving all church groups.

The purpose of the series is to use points of established need to bring about meaningful contact between the GOSPEL of God in Jesus Christ and YOUNG PEOPLE. Underlying the total effort is a concern that youth throughout the English-speaking world can be helped to see that the Gospel of Christ is the core of life itself in all its realities.

Unique to this publication effort is the use that is made of research findings. These describe the specific need to which each book is addressed as well as the youth most concerned about this need. Thus a writer is helped to speak more directly to the actual conflicts, values, and beliefs of an important segment of youth.

The significance of this series is enhanced by the scholarship and pastoral concern of the authors. Their grasp of the fields in which each writes enables them to speak with authority, establishing the series as a basic reference in the area of youth work.

Contents

Part I: The Cry of Cain

I knew Cain and others like him when I lived in New York. Cain speaks for himself in the story that follows. He also speaks for others. He expresses the search of my own youth and probably of yours. "Cain" may seem a strange name for a modern hero. Still, his name describes his character. He is a fugitive and a brother. As I look back into my own past I discover a close kinship with Cain. Through his experience and my own I seek for ways to talk about life and feel life with young people I meet.

I will let Cain tell his own story. He tells it freely in his own style. He has his own agnostic kind of approach to life. He invites us to strain ourselves with him in his quest for genuine meaning as a human being. *Part I* of this book, then, is his story related in his way. In *Part II* the scene and the style changes. Cain fights to overcome the offers of life from the chaplain. These conversations with Cain relate to the very questions Cain raised in his struggle to be someone. The segments of the conversation correspond to the segments of Cain's own story.

Are we persons or puppets in this day and age? Is God but a game? How do we learn our true identity as persons? Does Jesus Christ really change our lives? These are but some of the questions young people fling at me. These, then, are some of the questions that lie behind the cry of Cain and the search of the chaplain. However, between the Cain I know and the Christ I know there is a chasm. This book is an effort to bridge that gap, first by listening to Cain tell his own story and then by permitting an honest chaplain to grapple with Cain in conversation.

Go ahead, Cain, we're listening.

One. I WAS AN ACCIDENT

I was an accident,
a forgotten accident
at the end of a long line of accidents.
I didn't ask to be born.
Neither did my puny father
or my whining baby sister,
whose hair and dress
were dirty shreds of brown.

But we were there,
thrown together in a damp heap,
a pile of living bodies
smothered by the falling plaster
of a sour cellar apartment
in the corner of our city,
New York City.

Have you ever been to New York
and seen the gray blood
which seals the cold cement
in gray streets,
gray walls,
and gray eyes?

My mother was there, too.

She seemed to belong,
like worn parts of the house.
I suppose mothers are like that
in old houses.

My mother was strong and lumpy,
drooping at the chin
and eyes,
like some aged frog.
She liked to wear bright slacks
and sit behind the kitchen table
smoking Camel after Camel after Camel.

She was always there,
like the refrigerator
or the bathroom basin.

From the beginning
I knew I was an accident.
I could feel it
like the compound pimples
checkered on my face.

Time and time again
as I crept
into the room
my mother would rise,
sprawl her body
across the table,
and scream at me:

"You bitch of a kid,
you bitch."

Sometimes she'd brew for days inside
until
vibrating at the gills
her fuming lungs would swell,
explode,
and splatter words across the city walls.

"You dirty little bastard, you,"
she'd cry
and cry again.

The neighbor's dog would whimper
on his sacred mat.

Thank God, we had a cat.

After nights like that
I would sit alone
staring at the cracks
that crawled across our ceiling,
waiting . . .
waiting for a word,
a mother's word,
a healing word.

In the movies there's a hero
who can always stand alone
as tough as steel
and bold as stone.

"To be a hero," said one guy,
"you must learn to make something of yourself."

I'm not a hero
and I haven't met many kids who are,
kids who could face the sick world
and all its crooked sneers
by bragging they are men.

I was still alone
at the bottom of the pile
and I had the sickest feeling
that I could never
make something of myself

no matter how I tried.
Never!

Then, one night,
a night dredged up from the past,
a new struggle began.

The telephone rang.

My mother answered.

"Yes?"

"What's happened this time?"
she asked.

She listened on the phone,
her thick jaw sagging slowly.

I listened at the door,
squirming like an anxious little dog.

"My God,"
she growled in pain,
and stumbled from the house.

I sat beside the window
of our smeared brick house
that stood attached
to a long brick row of houses,
hideous monuments
to another generation
of unhappy lives.

I watched my mumbling mother
waddle down the pavement
to catch the corner bus
and join a dozen dazed women
staring frozen at the floor.

I was scared and weak.

I don't know why . . .
but I was.

I couldn't be a hero.
I couldn't make myself
into a big man.

How do you go about making yourself
into something,
into anything?

How?

What could I make?

Nothing.

Someone had made my transistor
and I thanked him for that.

Someone had made the street,
the lights, the cars,
the supermarkets,
and the bars.

Someone had!

In a church Sunday school
a teacher told us once
that God had made the sky and sun.

So what!

I couldn't make a thing.

All I remember about Sunday school
is a weasel-faced teacher
we called Weasel-Face.

She would tell us with a frown
that firing rubber bands
at harmless girls
was a sort of sin.

I knew those girls weren't harmless
and I have the scars
tattooed on my legs to prove it.

It was usually late
when my mother came home,
fell through the door,
and threw the squashed ground beef
into a snarling pan.

That afternoon
I planned to wander down
to the old ball park
and watch the little leaguers
scream their futile orders at each other.

As I hit the bottom step
where my sister leaves her doll,
a police car scraped the littered curb
and a line of nodding heads
protruded smugly
from the second-story windows.

I hid behind a panel van
and peered between the crowd
to see my mother
squeeze herself
out of the sparkling police car

between the gurgling crowd of bodies,
and up through the leering doorway
to her bedroom.

Two stiff policemen dragged my father
from the car,
across the sidewalk,
up the stairs,
and through the door.

Policemen always come in pairs
when they come to visit us.

Strange to say,
they brought my father home
instead of taking him to jail.

"I'm sending for a doctor,"
I heard one copper snarl.

He slammed the door of his car
and crawled away,
escaping from our world.

When the people had dispersed
and the incident
was being duly glorified
by the glow of gossips' eyes,
safe inside,
I bolted for the door
that sealed my mother's bedroom
from my life.

I gave a timid tap,
afraid to speak
or yell.

"Come in," she sobbed.

I came.

This time, please try to see,
her tears were not the same.

My father was a blotchy white,
his mouth agape,
his eyes fixed in a twisted stare.

"An attack," my mother said.

My father just lay there.

The doctor came to see him.

An hour later he was dead.

He didn't ask to die
any more than you or I.

He didn't, I tell you.

He didn't ask to die.

A moldy minister came
and talked to Mother
about the will of God.

He didn't help.

"Your husband was a good man,
Mrs. Brown," he said.

Well, that's a joke.

My father wasn't any better
than any other father I had met.

Most fathers I have met
are never home for long.
And those that are
will lounge before a TV face
and stare into its eye
until they're hypnotized
and snore.

Fathers have a way of saying,
"Sorry, kid,"
and leaving you behind
beside a tired mother
who is broken by the fights,
the fears,
the cold wars
her husband scatters in his wake.

Fathers are a fake!

I cried when my father died.

I don't understand the reason
or the psychology of it all.
I simply cried.

Everyone cried.

At the funeral I saw the brown earth
beneath the crackling carpet
of imitation grass
which covered the mound.

My father joined the lifeless ground,
captured in a wooden shell.

"He is planted as a seed,"
the black man said,
pouring forth his words into the air.
"And God will raise him as a plant
on the resurrection day."

Ridiculous thought.

It wasn't worth the trouble
anyway,
even if some hidden power
could re-create the dead.

I figured if he left them there
he'd be ahead.

The minister wrapped his arm around my mother,
which is really quite a feat,
and said, "Be brave."

My mother handed him an envelope
and sent that stranger off again,
untouched
and paid.

I suspect my little sister
hardly knew what happened
since she hardly knew my father.

We simmered back in a limousine,
sleek and black,
grinning at the colored cars
that squirmed along the highway.

My mother tried at first
to recollect the time
my father was exalted
for saving several people from a fire.

But that was all
she could recall.

The conversation died.

I reached my room in silence
and hugged my shining black transistor
that with a switch,
a cold command,
could take me to another land
where no one knows the beat of death,
the breathless rhythm of the grave . . .
and no one cares.

Across the vacant lot
the toughest guys,
and those who would be like them,
cry aloud their sympathy:
"You're just like one of us now, kid.
You only have your God
to be your father now,
and He won't give you half the trouble."

If God was anything, I thought,
He certainly wasn't a father.

I knew what a father was like
and I had no plans to be one . . .
so why should God?

Later,
the lawyer stalked in,
talked,
and stalked out.

We had no money.
I would have to work.
I would have to provide
for my mother.

I would have to be the breadwinner.

That's what the lawyer said.

I would have to play God.

The night passed slowly
and words from my subconscious . . .
strange words stirred
by the funeral,
by my father's death,
by something . . .
came to the surface.

They were words about God
holding conference long ago
and deciding:
"Let us make man
and let him rule for us."

Yes, that's the game,
to rule like God,
to take His place.

"Mother," I said,
"let's have a conference."

My mother went out into the night
unimpressed.

In the cover of the dark
I felt determined
not to be an accident
from that day on.

It was a desperate move
and a dangerous game.

But then,
what the hell,
what did I have to lose?

Two. GOD IS A GAME

God is a game,
a long game
without dice or partners.

It's a game we play
with emotions and bravado
in the silence of our room.

It's a game we play
with little people
dancing in our hands.

It was a new game for me.

My bulging mother lay
half naked
around the yellow mattress
where my dying father had fallen
three days before.
Her matted hair
crawled wildly
across her battered face
and deep into her open throat.

"I'm off to find a job,"
I said, yelling in her ear,
"get up and make the bed."

She gave a short crude snort,
a flinching shudder
from within her bowels,
and sank into her heavy frame.

That was the first time in my life
I had even dared
to tell my mother what to do.

As I stepped outside the house
beneath the bright blue morning sky
I sensed a new exhilaration,
a sudden twinge of power
and control.

The only guy I really knew
was the lanky fellow down the street
whose face was torn with holes.
I bounced up to his place
while he was still asleep.

It took a while
before the guy broke through the door
and looked me in the face
as if I'd smashed a law,
or something.

"Heh, listen, kid.
Don't bother me,
I gotta' go to work," he coughed.

"Can I come with you, Joe?"
I tried to say,
"I want to find a job."

"O.K." he said.
But, gosh, he looked a slob.

Joe worked up in Central Park
where people go to walk their anxious dogs
and throw their picnic lunch.

He introduced me to his supervisor,
a paunchy bag of air
who puffed his orders and his pipe
in the rapid rhythm
of a big executive.

From the first
I saw that he was also playing God
in a crooked sort of way,
with different rules than mine.

The paunchy super handed me a huge bag
with a hoop around the top
to keep the sack wide open.
I held the sack against my side
and in my right hand took a lengthy stick
to which a spike had been attached.

I ventured forth
as if I were a mighty Roman soldier
whose spear and shield
meant
destiny and fame.

I speared a million candy wrappers,
New York Times,
and torn silk stockings
while my super sat
and sucked a bottle in the bushes.
There was always someone in the bushes.

I took a sort of pride, at first,
in cleaning up the world
and letting everybody know

I was the new assistant gardener
in the greatest park on earth.

I learned to know the ways
of all the beasts who came
to seek the cover of the park,
the wolves that howl,
the cats that prowl,
the dogs that bark.

I watched them come and go
and scatter if I came too near
with my ancient spear.

Animals, you see, are queer.

I hardly saw my moping mother
through that first long week,
except to eat the hot dogs
and the jelly-bread
that gave us solid sustenance
for the daily fight ahead.

On Friday night
I knew she would be waiting
for the money on my hip.

I was relishing the plan I had
to demonstrate my role
as head of all
and master of our land.

I was sure my little sister
would have to be impressed.

But did she really matter?

I meandered home
across the park,
viewing all the lawns and tidy walks,
the gardens and the sky I ruled,
and dreaming of a victory,
the conquest of my world.

But dreams are brave thoughts
that die stillborn
in weak hearts.

My dreams, I said, would never die
or be tossed beneath the shrubs
like a bottle
or a bra.

They say that money talks,
and I was wise enough to know
that what I heard

was just as much my mind
as the money on my hip
rustling refrains.

I swaggered from the park
through the swirling crowd
where metal, dust, and men
swelled into an endless stream
of near collisions.

Then, as I swung the corner
to the sidestreet where I lived,
three guys with hairy chins
walked along beside me
as if I were a friend.

I didn't need a friend.

I didn't need anyone.

I didn't want anyone,
but this was three to one.

"Think that you can face your mother, kid?"
the big guy said.

"Know how to handle her, my boy?"
the weedy sucker to my right supplied.

I leaned against the nearest wall
and quelled my urge to fight.

"We know just what it's like, kid,"
the big guy rattled on.
"The time soon comes for men like us
to stand alone
and make our parents understand
just what it means
to be a modern man."

But how did that guy know
the very thoughts I had?

How could he psych me out?

How could he?

"Wise up, my boy,"
the sucker said,
"and take advice from us."

"We've got the stuff,"
the big guy yawned,
"to really build you up.
If you want to make it big,
like an undercover man
or a cool executive,

then take a little weed, man,
and you'll never be the same."

Now someone else had changed the rules.
The game was still the same.

They could see that I was scared,
writhing in my boots,
but wondering all the while
what it might be like
to follow their advice.

"Just try it once,"
the big guy said,
"You can't get hurt
this way.
And your ma won't know
the secret of your power."

The third guy threw a pack
in the middle of my palm
and scrutinized my moves.

When I saw the power in my hand
to step another rung
toward my goal,
I reached behind me
for the money in my pocket.
I held the wad between my fingers
and didn't see
how close the circle now had grown.

A sudden jerk.

A swift retreat.

All my money disappeared with them,
and all my hopes fled down the street.

A fresh black hole
began to open in my brain,
a churning hole,
a swirling drain.

I felt as if I had exposed
my body to the world.

Driven by a fixed and empty stare
I floated home
and fell across my bed
to hide my lost dreams in a pillow.

Pillows are almost as great
as transistors.

My mother crashed into the door
and fixed her bloated arms

upon her bloated hips
and croaked:

"Well, where's the dough?"

I tried to turn
and blame it on those hairy guys
who caught me off my guard.

My mother slammed her loaded fist
across my ear
and screamed an ugly oath:
"God damn you, kid,
you're no better than your father was."

I heard her leave
and slam the door.

She always slammed the door.

The darkness smothered me
and I wanted to explode!

I think I almost did.

I woke next morning
to the thunderous sound
of the landlord pounding on the wall
in the same uneven rhythm
as the beating on my brain.

We knew what that would mean.

His visit was the last chance,
the last offer,
and I had failed.

We had no way to stall him,
no money,
no promises,
no deal.

Eviction is a strange song
that never dies
but keeps repeating in your heart
every time you fail,
like the melody of a girl
who sings the blues.

I thought of running off
and living with a bunch of guys
somewhere.

My sister hugged her doll
and watched me suffer.

She liked to watch me suffer,
the little brat.

I flipped the black transistor switch,
only to hear the rapid beat
of another harsh guitar
blare a while . . .
shudder . . .
crack . . .
and softly die.

The battery was dead.
A cold silence
surrounded by a black cloud
filled the room.

At last
my mother took the phone
puffing tightly on her Camel
as she squinted at the dial.

"Hi, John," she said,
trying to be polite,
and make the smallest talk I've ever heard
from a woman of her size.

"Do you have a room, somewhere,
just to help us out
until we find another place to live?"

"For the sake of all the kids."

"We'll pay you back."

"Of course, we will."

"Thanks, John; thanks a million."

My mother cried.

An hour later John drove up
in a Plymouth station wagon
and carted off
what little things we hoped to save
before the landlord's tough men came.

This John was Uncle John,
or so my mother said.

His head was square and bald
and he had a way of laughing
almost every time he spoke,
as though he knew a secret
or a joke.

This uncle, Mother said,
handled real estate in Queens,
which means
he bought and sold old houses
at a pretty profit.

He slapped me on the back
and said, "Let's go, young man."

He even kissed my sister,
which I couldn't understand.

And my mother cried again.

The car stormed off into the freeway
where motor cars
like molecules
swirl around a clover leaf
and speed toward disaster.

I had no notion
where the ride would end.

But end it did,
and we found ourselves located
for that duration
in a pair of rooms
above bald Uncle John's garage.

When I thought about it much
there seemed to be no reason
why my uncle took the trouble
to help a family like us,
who must have been a worthless gang
in his successful eyes.

I daresay he felt big,
magnanimous,
and brave.

The strangest thing of all
were the clothes he bought
for us to wear.

You'd think he had been
waiting for us all
to live out there.

"These are the kind of clothes
we wear out here.
You'll seem like one of us now, kid,
a part of this fine suburb."

"And if you like
you can come with us to church tomorrow,"
my uncle added slowly.

My God,
I knew there was a hitch somewhere,
another trap.

Three. LIFE IS A MASK

Everyone I met
wore a new mask,
a new clue
to what they feared.

In that suburb of Queens
I could see these masks more clearly
than deep within my own dark city,
where frayed faces
and torn screens
were as familiar to me
as the faded wallpaper.

I suppose I always knew
that people posed
like puppets for the world.
But it hadn't bothered me
until then.

I had the feeling
that somewhere below their smiles
every one of them
was much the same as I was.
They, too, had blood
and bleeding hopes in their veins.
But, if that were true,
how could they tolerate
these tricks
and change of face?

How?

For meals
we used to
sit like cold dummies,
pressing our stomachs
hard against the covered table
in Uncle John's house.

We had napkins made of linen,
and butter knives with butter,
manners with our mushrooms,
and "pass the salt" with smiles.

The first night there
I knocked the laughing beets
across the shiny shirt

of my smirking cousin Tony
who spluttered like a dying motor,
grabbed his linen napkin,
but caught the tablecloth instead.

For quite a while
dignity was dead.

"Accidents will happen,"
my aunt exclaimed.

"Never mind," said Uncle John.

I knew quite well
that he and everyone in sight
wanted to explode and cry,
"Get out of here
and get to hell!"

And that's precisely
what I would have liked to do.

So there we sat,
glorified in beets,
trying hard to smile
a worthless smile.

The next morning
I watched their blinking faces
trying to adjust to another day
and find another mask.
to fit the Sunday mood.

As I glanced around the breakfast meal
it seemed to me
I first began to see
the real faces of that grinning gang.

Uncle John, erect and bald,
was nothing but a seal,
slippery in his Sunday suit,
croaking forth his wisdom:
"Today's the Lord's day,
and so we leave at ten
to go to church."

I wondered how a seal would sound
singing hymns in church.

All too soon, alas,
I didn't need to wonder any more.

Aunt Marie,
a basket full of hair
ballooned upon her head,
was a peacock on the prowl.
Instantly I knew

she was a proud and prudish bird
who could not bear to have her feathers touched,
but had to be admired . . .
from afar.

I wished that somehow
I could spill the beets once again
and turn that stiffened peacock
into a speckled hen.

Cousin Tony was a wriggling weasel
poking forth his nose across his plate,
or should I say his snout,
and peering sideways
from behind his thick square glasses.

My own mother was a brown bear,
hairy and heavy,
sagging over her plate,
over her chair,
over everything.

I'd rather live with a sagging bear
than a cross-eyed weasel anytime.

At last we reached the church
and I could see
a great line of performing seals
slithering down the aisle
accompanied by more peacocks
and many more weasels.

Within a few minutes
all the animals were rigid and ready,
except for an occasional rustling of feathers
or the squeaking of one wicked little weasel.

The wind moaned in the organ pipes,
the animals groaned in the pews,
and the heavens howled above.

Had none of these people
heard the noise
that my brave transistor
spits into the world
to waken our senses
and give men life?

I felt so stupid
in my pew,
trying hard
to sit and rise
or rise and sit
for this and that

or that and this
whenever others did
without an intermission.

When the minister stepped into his box
I sensed a sudden silence,
a hint that things would change.

Change they did.
A sorry stream of words
were fired across the room
to batter people senseless
in their seats.

This preacher talked about a guy
who grabbed his father's cash
and spent it all
at nightclubs here in New York City.
When all his funds were gone
he found a job feeding pigs.
You can't find jobs like that
in New York any more.

Anyhow, he went back home to see his father
who thought the guy was dead.

His father was elated
and threw the guy a party . . .
as if he hadn't had enough
of parties, clubs, and dancing.

There was something strange
about the fact that any father
welcomed home a kid like that.
It made me think
that maybe not all fathers
were quite the same as mine.

Nowadays people don't really have
a father to come home to. . . .
You have to learn to make it on your own.
There is no other way.

I'll bet old Uncle John,
or any of those well-fed seals
sitting in that church,
would never want me back
if I stole the cash
from their golden offering plate.

What a waste.

I had the feeling
that the father
which the minister meant
was really God.

But I hadn't stolen any of God's money . . .
so I didn't see much point in the story.

When we came out of church
I met Tony's weasel friends
who looked at me as if I had boils
or some dogs' disease.

I snapped at them
and went back to the car.

I watched as everyone changed clothes
after lunch . . .
changed clothes and changed masks.

Tony kept saying
that church was good
because it helps people to be good people.
He said God loves people
who go to church.
He said I should have been nice
to his friends.
He said. . . .

Well, I knew he wasn't coming clean with me.
His speeches were a big deal
to impress me,
to make me look dirty and cheap.

"Your church is stupid,"
I cried. "Stupid."

"Maybe some day you'll learn
to love God the way we do,"
smiled Tony.

I was getting mad.
He thought he was so damn superior.
He thought he had God
all to himself.

I wanted to expose him,
to tear off his face
and uncover his dirty blood.

I wanted to kill him
to show him how much God loved him.
I felt a new urge,
like the lurch of a train,
or the rising pitch of a siren
on a police car.

The urge grabbed me
and made me shake all over.
I heard it inside me,

I felt it
and I swung my fists
into his weasel face,
battering his glasses into his cheeks
and forcing his bleeding lips
between his weasel teeth.

I couldn't stop.
I couldn't.

When I did, he was still,
so very white
and silent
and still.

Do you ever get mad at someone
and beat and beat your fists
on your bed
or on the wall?

I beat my fists
on his head,
until he didn't move.

I don't really understand why.

After that there was only one thing
left to do: to run . . .
to run from all these people with masks.

They wouldn't understand,
they wouldn't even try.

I ran down the road,
on and on,
forever and ever.

At the subway station
I took a car up north,
up through Manhattan,
through crowds of commuters
who stood still and quiet
staring at the walls.

My heart kept running,
trying to escape.

But no one looked at me,
or worried,
or bothered.

Hour after hour
I wandered through the city
looking at sleeping autos
or frozen figures in store windows.

The load was getting heavier on my back
and I was getting weary.

I can't explain the load,
but it was there,
on my back,
in my head,
and on my hands.

So what,
even if I had beaten and killed that weasel,
why should I care?

No one cared about me.

I would have to get tough.

But I wasn't really tough,
or strong,
or big,
and I knew it.

I was weak
and I carried a new load.

Late that first night
I found myself
back in Central Park.

I knew where to find a place to sleep,
deep in the heavy bushes and ivy beds
where I had seen drunks asleep before.

God,
I was cold and hungry.

I fell asleep in the ivy
and lost my fear for a few short hours.

Next morning
I found enough small change
to buy a roll for breakfast
and gulp it down.

At eight a.m.
I found myself, dazed and stiff,
reporting to the paunchy super
to begin my work that week.
I stood before him
as I had the week before
strangely unaware of my predicament.

Suddenly it dawned on me
that police might come
and grab me there.

I was just about to run
when the super looked me in the eye,
puffed his stub,
and spat into the ground.

"You'll never make it, kid,
if you act as though you're scared," he said.
"Make them think you're tough and sure,
with a secret weapon
up your sleeve."

With that I ran again,
ran until I fell
with a pain across my face
and the burden on my back
imbedded in my bones.

The super's dismal words
spun across my brain
like the ribbon of a teletype,
swinging back and forth again.

"You'll never make it, kid,
if you act as though you're scared. . . ."

A scared kid
is a marked man.

Now,
I would need to wear a mask
if I was to survive.

A mask?

My God,
how ugly!

And yet it seemed
there was no other way.

It was a question of survival.

But was it just another mask
or something hidden deep inside me
coming to the surface?

Was it really me?

And so
I wore the toughest mask
that I could mold
as I tried to find another job
or steal a scrap of food
from the kitchen of a restaurant
or a diner.

When things got very rough
I could always play the game

of groundsman at the zoo
and steal what food I could
from the cages
or the pens.

Then,
one cold blue night,
I tried to crawl inside
a pen full of straw
to find a place to sleep
within the zoo.

By chance,
the cops were combing through the park
that night
in search of wild kids with knives.

One policeman caught me in the cage
and dragged me to a station
as a member of the gang
they were chasing through the streets.

Stations ooze a feeling
of hatred and distrust.
And there it's hard to show you're tough
when everyone
is acting tougher still.

Every cop looks like a rhinoceros,
hard and wrinkled and black,
poking out a brutal nose
into everybody's business.

You try to act tough.

You say nothing,
but you want to ask for help.
You are scared,
but you wear a mask anyway.

Lord, was I scared?

Somehow they found out my name
and I waited.

They threw me into a cell
that smelled of sweat.

I didn't know why I was there,
but I was,
a kid thrown in among the members of a gang
picked up that night
in the park.

Now I *had* to be tough
and wear the mask of Cain.

Four. INVOLVEMENT IS A PRISON

All men are prisoners
trapped by their past,
their feelings,
their frustrations.

They beat against the masks
which they themselves have made
to protect their tender ego
from the world of stone-faced people
who seem tougher by the year.

The men inside a city prison
are much the same
as those who live outside its buckled walls
and think that they are free.

I know
because I know them both!

I was still wearing my leather mask,
testing my toughness
against the sharp edges
of a broken world.

Everyone I met
was like another broken bottle,
like the jagged edge of a can
that rips the flesh
but keeps on shining
with a smile.

At first the prison inmates watched me,
cold, steady,
testing my nerves,
my breeding,
and my guts.

I was scared again,
but my mask had now become part of me
and I didn't flinch.

When a guy with rotten brown teeth
stared at me,
holding a slab of bacon
between his gritted gums,
I stared back.

It seemed like an hour,
or more.

At last
he plunged a fork into his shivering egg
and sucked what slimy yolk was left
between his dented teeth,
and spat the bacon on his plate.

At least he didn't
spit it in my face.

Guys in prison
are usually in a bad mood
in the morning.

And so are all the wardens,
by God.

A twisted kind of guy,
with a screwed-up hairlip,
was the first to really grab at me
and test my quivering guts.

As I rose to leave the table
he shot a fork into my back
to see if I would flinch,
or scream,
or squeal.

"What's the matter, punk?" he asked,
"have you never been in jail?"

I looked around and snarled,
"I'll slit your liver with my fingernail
if you call me punk again."

I would have to play it big, it seemed,
or else I'd end up dead.

I stewed inside
until we reached the bunks,
and a circle of the toughest kids
kept me under fire
with their eyes.

"What's your name?"

"What have you done?"

"Why are you here?" they asked.

I had the feeling, as I listened,
that the guys
who ran that group
had a standard of acceptance
that I had never seen before.

This was the inner ring
of a rebel teenage gang
rejected by the city.

I waited with a cold
and calculating pause,
sensing in myself somehow,
that they would have to know
how big I was
within the world of crime.

This was my hour,
my chance,
my time.

I knew my petty stealing in the park
would never mean a thing to them.

"I killed a kid," I said,
"with nothing but my hands."

I looked down at my hands.
They looked so small,
so weak,
so worthless.

But it worked.
The gamble paid off
and I was in . . .
a giant once again,
or so I thought.
I was a hero.

I had capitalized on my mistake,
and used my ugly work
to build myself a new image,
to fortify my mask
and make a prison wall around my mind.

I had really framed myself
this time.

"We don't believe you, kid,"
said the guy with
the screwed-up mouth.
"Well, read the city papers,"
I replied.

"I still think he's a punk,"
whined the boy with rotten gums,
who lay across the bed.
In a flash I could see
that my chances of victory were small
if I didn't soon attack.

Like an animal in pain
I lunged with my fist
and sank his thick blue lips
between his dirty teeth.

"Get up," cried all the gang.

But the Buddha lay there swallowing blood,
like a cow.

I waited,
scared and hot,
wondering whether
he would murder me,
or not.

Maybe he
was really just as scared inside
as I was.

My name was called over the loud speaker
and the final showdown
set aside
for yet another fatal day.

I was called into a room
to meet a man they called the chaplain,
or the teacher—
a guy who tried to be a buddy
but didn't quite know how.

He told me that my uncle
had heard that I was there in prison
and would try to get me out.
He said my mother had a job
at a laundry out in Queens.

I shrugged my slouching shoulders
and tried to act as cool
as I had been inside the cell.

My gruff response didn't seem
to bother him at all.
He kept on talking
as if I were a window or a wall.

"It's easy enough to act as though you're tough,"
said the teacher,
rambling on.

What the hell did he know anyway?
He hadn't been in prison.

"You can call yourself a real man, son,
when you can do the opposite
of what the gang demands
because you know you're right."

"What's right?" I snorted,
getting more involved,
even though I hadn't planned
to listen to the fool at all.

"God knows what's right,"
he mumbled.

"But God has never been in prison,"
I shouted like a kid
accused of lying.

"Are you sure?" replied the guy.
"Jesus Christ was in a prison,
beaten up and spat on by the guards,
whipped and taken out beside Jerusalem,
to die
like any other criminal."

"So?" I said.

"So He was really a marked man,
marked by God to set men free."

"Too bad!" I laughed.

"Too bad for you, young man,
for what He did was done for you as well."

"Oh shut up," I snarled beneath my breath.

When I went back to join the men inside,
I heard their old refrain.

"Did you get the bit
on Jesus Christ in prison?"

"And Jesus hadn't done a thing,
so that makes him quite a fake."

"But Jesus wouldn't fight at all,
so that really makes him chicken."

"See if Jesus Christ can pull the strings
to get you out of here!"

They jumped on Jesus Christ
with a cruel kind of malice
that I had never heard before . . .
at least their leaders did.

None of the others had the guts
to state their inner feelings.

"What did you tell the teacher?"
cried the twisted guy with glee.

I had to keep my front,
and so I had to bluff again.

I was sinking deeper by the hour
into my own prison pit.

"I told the creep to go to hell," I said.

They seemed to be impressed,
but well . . .

"I told him I would rather be in prison
than with Jesus Christ in heaven."

Which was partly true, I guess,
since I didn't want to be in
either place.

My words were like a poisonous gloom
which sank between the men.

They spluttered wildly for a minute,
half repeated what I said,
and then fell silent
in the gloom.

I wondered how many of them
liked to be tough with their peers,
tough and alone,
but weak and alone inside,
weak like I was.

The next day everything changed,
like the end of one life
and the beginning of another.

All of the youths were taken off
to a huge new prison farm
that was like a short course in hell,
or so the rumor went.

They all went,
except me.

"Your uncle will take care of you,"
announced the warden.

You have another chance.

For a while I felt like Noah,
left behind,
the last survivor
in a world of tough giants,
left behind
like the pilot of a plane wreckage
when all the passengers are dead.

Left behind
by the grace of . . .
my uncle.

Why?

My uncle could never take care of me.
It was impossible to think so
after what I had done to his kid.

He came.

And we drove off.

I was out of prison,
but I wasn't free.

Five. "HI" IS A BIG WORD

The world is a ball
of broken string
with loose ends that fall,
unable to meet.

Every day
we yank and strain
until another strand
is severed
or frayed.
Our friends,
our families,
our heroes,
our lords,
are left in our path
like burnt ropes
and loose cords.

The world is a ball
of broken string
and God, if He's there,
has left us dangling.

I knew that I had broken
the ties
between my uncle's household
and myself.

Blood is not enough
to seal such broken lives,
especially blood
spilled on the road.

As I drove in the car
with my uncle,
I had the feeling
that our minds
were like two
live crackling ends
of torn electric wires.

Inside, I was rather glad to see him,
but I knew there could be
nothing but enmity between us
and hard bitter feelings.

Surely he hated me.

Why was he taking me home?

To torture me? How?
With silence?
With kindness?
With threats?
With God?

My uncle's car slithered smoothly down the highway,
oblivious to
the broken circuit
between the people in the car.

"Did they treat you well?"
he ventured.

"Sure," I said,
keeping my distance
and my place.

"Your mother's been very worried, boy,"
he said with some sincerity.

What was I supposed to say to that?
I knew how deep her worry had extended in the past . . .
to the bottom of her purse!
At least that's what I thought.

I was silent,
screaming inside.

"We'll have to buy some new clothes
before this afternoon," he added.

What did he mean by that?
This afternoon?

The word had never sounded quite so terrible before,
so frightening,
so ominous.

Why should I feel scared
or lousy anyway?
I had faced the roughest lot there was,
the Angel gang from New York City.
I had faced them in a jail
and survived their vicious plots.

But this was sort of different.
I had the urge to run again,
to leave
and never see the afternoon.

But a deeper drive to see my mother
kept me sober for a time.

We drove into a shopping center

near my uncle's house in Queens
and bought another pair of pants,
a shirt,
a tie,
and brand new shoes.

They couldn't tolerate me
as I was,
a slob who made the news.

I looked respectable with clothes,
and I wore a shining mask
I'd forgotten how to use.

When we swung into the driveway
I saw my weeping mother squash her heavy cheeks
between the window frames
and swing her lumpy arm
as though it were a club.

She had never waved like that to me before.
There seemed to be a plot afoot
to smother me with sweet affection
as though I were a poodle
who had broken from his leash
and everyone was whistling,
calling sweetly,
to cajole him to a corner
where he could be attacked
and united with his chain
once more.

But I wasn't born a poodle
and I wanted to be free,
free from my past,
my fears,
my tears,
and my future.

There was nowhere left to run . . .
nowhere.

I was in a corner
lined with a strange kindness.

My mother enveloped me in sobs
and cries
and rolls of fat.

My aunt said, "Welcome back,"
with a kind of dry choke
that almost brought a tear
before my eyes.

But the severed ties

within the family
could not be mended that way.

The broken body of a youth
still lay between us,
and a fierce struggle to forget
could easily become
a vicious stream of curses
if I spoke my spinning mind
about the way I felt.

The whole thing was half unreal,
and my mind was
like a dream,
a reel of film
spitting forth
its flickering frames.

The food upon the lunch table
struck a new responsive chord.
Like that lost and hungry poodle
I devoured meat
while others picked their bones.

Most of the time we ate in silence,
until my mother asked:

"How did they treat you, son?"

I stared at my uncle.

"Did they treat you all right?" she continued.

"Sure," I said,
quite certain now
that the questions had been rigged
and I was being programmed
for correction.

A word or two was said
about a group of kids at church
who wanted me to come that evening
and join their local fun.

Once more
I had the urge to run.

"Let's do the dishes," said my aunt,
"and we'll soon be at the hospital."

I was left hanging
again.

The hospital?

Why were we going to the hospital?

No one seemed ill.

I don't ever recall visiting a hospital . . .
only the outpatient's ward.

Why wouldn't they tell me?

They all knew why,
but I didn't.

It was dirty.

I began to hate them all again.

My new collar was getting tighter
around my clean neck.

We drove down the highway,
swung around a long lawn,
and stepped into the hospital.

A hospital is a torture chamber,
a spaceship with glass floors,
glaring white beds,
glaring white walls,
and white people
racing past each other in the glare,
the icy glare.

Strange heads protrude at odd angles
from the white beds,
and bottles of liquid
hang suspended like huge bugs
over their heads.

Periodic smiles
like little cracks
would break the cold glass screen
which insulated people from reality
in that sparkling tomb.

Sixth floor,
east wing,
room 602,
behind a screen,
against the wall,
hidden in the pillow
we saw a head.

Over its eyes
was a wide bandage
that almost covered its face.

"Tony," said Uncle;
and my mind collapsed.

A million words,
thoughts,
questions,

doubts,
cries invaded my head
and stormed my brain.

"We've brought your cousin Cain
to see you."

Tony wasn't dead!
Why hadn't they told me?
Was this their way of torturing me,
making me sweat out my guilt?

"Won't you say Hi?"

He should have said, "Hell."
I had beaten his face
and ruined his eyes
and he should say "Hi?"

That just doesn't happen!
I was no fool.
They were squeezing my blood
by their tender displays
of concern.

Boy, I had a lot to learn!

Tony stretched forth his hand
reaching out in blind reproach,
pointing five fingers
at my heart . . .

Like five knives . . .

Like death!

I couldn't stand it . . .
my mask was crumbling
and two ends of my life
were almost united in a clasp
of hope
that was impossible,
ridiculous,
frightening. . . .

I stared at his hand
for the count of ten,
and ran . . .

down the silver hall,

my footsteps echoing,

ringing,

haunting,

the hospital walls.

I flew through the doors
and onto the street
back to the subway
where I had been before
so many times.

I couldn't understand;
I couldn't think.

The last time I ran from him
I was running from death,
but this time
I was running from life,
I guess.

Was that it?
Was that true?

What was true?

Where were the answers?

Pieces of the past few days flew at each other
like so many arrows,
like the slices of a dream
that kept eluding my full consciousness:

. . . the game of God . . .
. . . my loose mask . . .
. . . the long road back . . .
back where. . . ?
back to the beginning . . .
that foolish sermon
about the guy feeding pigs
and a father who wanted him back . . .
. . . the load on my back . . .
. . . the teacher at the prison . . .
and the bit about Jesus Christ
in prison . . .
God . . .
no, I can't take that road . . .
why did my uncle take me back. . . ?
to crush me?
why didn't they tell me
that Tony was alive,
in the hospital. . . ?
so that I wouldn't run
until I faced him. . . ?
. . . where is the door,
the light,
the future. . . ?
God, that's what Tony is thinking . . .
now I'm thinking about him . . .
where? . . . where? . . . where?

I looked up
after hours of wandering,
and subconsciously I knew
I was coming back
to the one man
who had not been bluffed by my front.
I was returning to the chaplain.

I entered the police station
and asked for the chaplain.

"That's a switch," laughed the cop,
and lifted the phone.

For an hour I waited,
pacing,
almost walking out a dozen times.

When he saw me
he smiled,
and I almost reacted in hate. . . .

By then I knew
it was simply too late.

"Loose ends," I said,
"a life full of broken ends . . ."

I didn't know what to say.

"A covenant," said the chaplain.
"You need a covenant."

"What on earth is that?"

"When you tie people together
with promises that can't be broken . . .
when you tie them together
with forgiveness. . . . "

That was too much!

But yet . . . I thought.

"God tied Abraham to Himself with promises,"
he continued.

"God ties you to Himself with even better promises,
with forgiveness.

"He forgave you
when Jesus Christ died in your place.

That was forgiveness at work!

Its time for you to begin saying Hi!"

I went out into the night
and wondered how . . .

How could I ever go back
and tie the loose ends
with knots of forgiveness.

It was ridiculous . . .

too ridiculous to believe.

I sat in the park
and laughed at the endless sky.

Part II: The Conversations with Cain

There is much of Cain in all of us. We cannot shrug our shoulders and forget about him. Cain is our brother. We know him from his story. Oh, I suppose I could dissect his story for you and show you how similar many of his experiences are to the events in Genesis 1-12. But that would be pretty rather than personal. We are concerned about brothers like Cain, men who uncover raw realities within our own lives. How do we face the world with them? How do they and we become real individuals in a world that threatens to make us robots? How do we survive as persons worthy of the name?

The story of Cain ends in his conversation with a chaplain who asks the impossible. He offers forgiveness as a center for life. What if we were to let this chaplain spin out his conversations with Cain? What if we were to eavesdrop on their struggle to understand Cain's experiences? What if we were to let that chaplain take Cain all the way back to Genesis 1-12 as a source for meaning? What if we were to encourage that chaplain to confront Cain with Christ? Would we laugh? Would we feel uncomfortable? Would we be willing to go through the agony needed to explain just what it means to be a whole person in Christ? Could we survive that kind of test for faith? Or is God but a futile game?

I invite you to join the struggle of Cain in his conversations with the chaplain in the next five chapters. I urge you to fight his battle with him . . . as your brother. If it appears to you that I seem to be that chaplain, you may not be far wrong. But don't let that discovery lull you into thinking that the chaplain's words are ready answers. Far from it. His words are some of the tentative convictions I have about being who I am. My questions are also Cain's questions. My thoughts are reflections of my own dilemma about meaning as a person. Meaning, I submit, is an individual thing, a personal touch. Yet, if what I have faced is what you are facing, the conversations between Cain and the chaplain may come alive and be as real as they were for me. Let's listen.

Conversation One: BACK TO THE BEGINNING

Want to talk about it, Cain?

No, I don't pretend to be
a better listener or talker
than anyone else.
But maybe, just maybe,
I've thought about these things, too,
and wondered why I was born.

Where do we find the answers?
Better still,
Where do we find the right questions?
Where?
By digging into the misty past
or peering into the foggy future?
There are massive chunks of history
behind us and ahead of us.
And we are born in the middle,
or so it seems . . . like accidents.
The world appears to be no more
than one enormous orphanage
full of illegitimate people.
Anonymous men and women
mill through the streets of New York.
Anonymous millions die of hunger
along the Ganges River in India.
People everywhere
become part of the scenery—
unnoticed,
unwanted,
untidy accidents of life.

I don't blame you for agreeing, Cain,
for seeing no plan in the world,
no special "something"
that gives us a real reason
to be part of this world.
In our day, too,
it's easy to feel worthless,
useless,
and out of place.

Perhaps the universe has run amok.
Perhaps we will all be ground to pieces
in its huge cogs.

55

Perhaps there is no goal to life
except death.
Perhaps . . .

Before we agree to that, Cain,
we ought at least to ask
whether anyone does see a plan
at work in the world,
or whether anyone does find meaning
in something around them.

Yes, perhaps it is a waste of time,
but if life is pointless anyway,
why not waste it wondering?

Cain,
let me suggest that we go all the way back
to the old story about creation
you learned as a kid.
That story seems to say
that in the beginning there was a plan
that made sense.

No, no. I can't prove it.
But we're not talking about math
or science
or evidence that we can put
under a microscope.
We're talking about meaning.
And meaning must be discovered
by searching and listening.

I'm convinced
there are clues
in the creation story of Genesis
to help us make that discovery.

The man who wrote Genesis One
believed that our universe was created
according to a master plan of God.
He had a great scheme for the universe
and a special purpose for all of life.

Unfair?
I suppose it is unfair
to introduce God without warning.

You want me to prove
that God really exists?
Well, I can't.

But does it matter at this point in the discussion?
The Bible doesn't bother
to prove the reality of God, either.

God is assumed
right from the beginning.
If you like, He is the beginning.
Perhaps He is far more,
but for now
let us call the beginning, "God."

No, I cannot prove there was a beginning
any more than you can.
But then again
there is no way to prove the opposite.
Anyway, I have to admit
that God is alive for me somehow.
There is a mystery to life,
there is a beginning for me,
there is a silent power
that preceded me
and caught me, somehow.
Let that much be granted
as we search for some sense
in this world.

Damn the beginning?
Maybe. But before you do that,
why not go back to the beginning
and see if we can find out something
about the roots of life itself.
The psychiatrist takes the patient
back to his childhood to find the real person.
The American historian leads us back
to our forefathers in Europe.
The anthropologist investigates
the habits of the Stone Age man.
The biologist traces our origins
to the earliest forms of life.
Each in his own way
is trying to discover just who we are
and why we live our life the way we do.

The writer of Genesis
claims to go back even further.
And he claims to go back in a different way . . .
not via science
or logic
or historical evidence
but via a word of God.

This man insists he is speaking for God.
He claims that God designed the world
and that our origins were not accidental
but deliberate.

How?
With a magic wand?
Well, not exactly a wand,
but a word,
or more precisely ten words.

What does that mean?
Let's put it like this:
The word of the president means power.
When he speaks, things happen.
If he wants action, he gets it.
And the writer in Genesis says
that the world happened
because God wanted it to happen.
Ten times in that creation story
we read: "And God said. . . . "
That word, claims the writer,
that spoken will of God,
was the beginning of everything.
In the beginning there was the Word
and the Word was the beginning . . .
and that was God.

All right, if you want to say it that way:
"In the beginning God did all the talking
and made something
out of the churning black waters
He found lying around."
But He didn't make the earth for fun . . .
or maybe He did . . .
maybe He made the earth
for man to inhabit
and for God to enjoy Himself with man.

You figure that God is not that human?
That He cannot enjoy himself?
That if He did organize the world
He is no more than a cosmic computer?
That He has no feelings
or concerns
or love for you?
That He programmed the world
for people to shuttle through life
as punch cards?
That we end up filed
in the memory bank of eternity?

So the question becomes—
Am I important in God's scheme of creation?
Am I personally involved?
Or am I just a punch card?

An anonymous piece of nature?
Another hunk of clay?

First of all,
let's ask whether the writer of Genesis
was intimately involved in the story of creation
when he told it to his people.
I guess we have to realize
he was discussing a specific problem with them,
and he wasn't talking directly with us.
The people he was addressing were Israelites
who had been tempted to worship gods
like the sky
or the sun
or the storm.
Israel's neighbors worshiped these gods
and Israel was regularly conquered
by mighty neighbors
like Assyria and Babylon.
Their gods seemed mightier
then the God of Israel.
They had far more exciting stories
about how the gods created the world
than Israel had.
Their gods were sexy
and wild
and fun to worship . . . or so it seemed.

Along comes the writer of Genesis
who tries to explain
that the world is not a mixture of gods
who keep things going
by sexual intercourse in heaven
or by fighting in the underworld.
In fact, he says,
God is not part of the world at all.
He is not the sun or the sky.
He preceded the world.
He is the beginning.
He is the mystery behind everything.
He is in, with, under, and outside the world.
But He is not the world.

Yes, indeed,
that was a message the Israelites needed to hear
time and time again.

That's not our problem, you say?
We don't worship nature?
We don't see gods everywhere?

I guess you're right.

We have trouble seeing God anywhere.
We have emptied the world of the old gods
and we've forgotten how to worship new ones.

But does that mean God is lost
and this story from Genesis is pointless?
Isn't it possible that,
although the problem of many gods
is not quite the problem we face today,
there is a deeper issue involved?
Maybe the question is "Why?"
Why did the writer want to get the gods
out of creation?
Why was it important
to put God at the beginning of things
. . . all alone?

Perhaps the answer is in the verdict
which God keeps passing
after each stage of the creation process.
Do you remember?
"Behold. It's very good."
Or if you will,
"Hey. It's really great."

Good for what? Great for whom?
Good for God and good for man.
The Israelite had to see the world
in a new light.
The world as such
wasn't full of fighting gods,
some good and some evil,
some wild and some fickle.
Rather, the earth was a mighty work of art . . .
and more.
It was created for man's enjoyment,
for man's good,
for man's laboratory . . .
and more.
It was made for man to rule.

You don't believe that
because it doesn't seem to happen?
Because we seem to be no more
than statues
and pawns?

Maybe,
but God made men in the image of God,
insists this thinker from Genesis.

What's the point of that idea?

Well,
after insisting that nothing was a god,
that nothing could be compared to God,
that everything else was created,
we might conclude
that man was no different from the animals.
No, says this writer.
There was something like God.
And that was man.
Man was not the same as the rest of creation.
He stood between God and creation.

That doesn't mean he was half god
and half man.
But he was made in the image of God.
An image was more than a statue
for ancient men.
It represented a god or a leader.
So man was to represent God on earth,
to be God's ruler on earth,
to take God's place on earth,
to reflect God's feelings on earth.

What kind of ruler?
A free agent or a puppet king?

A free agent!
That was the risk God took.
He put man in charge
and left Himself open to abuse.
Man was free to make the world
into something
or to wreck it completely.
God gave man the reins,
says the writer.
In the beginning
man was free . . . with God,
and for God.

It's not that way now?
Perhaps not.
But maybe it should be.
Maybe God's plan to put man in charge
and to let him control the world
is still what God wants.
Maybe God does want us
to be responsible agents
who will make the earth
a credit to its Maker.
Why should God expect us
to be puppets or pawns?

Why not grant the idea of this writer
and see God's plan as valid?
Why shouldn't man have a creative role
as ruler of the universe?
Why not?

Why not allow the possibility
that the word God speaks
still works,
still creates,
still begins things,
still summons us to be men like Him,
men in His image,
free to make something of this world?
Why not let God be the beginning
now
for us?

It's not that simple, you say?
It's a wonderful dream
to have all men free
to rule the world,
but it doesn't work that way?
The dream doesn't really involve you?
It doesn't give you any worth?
It doesn't give you individuality?

But perhaps it can, Cain.
Perhaps there's a way
to realize that dream.

But, first,
let's ask ourselves
why it isn't so simple,
why we cannot be free
the way God intended,
why we lose our sense of worth,
and why we end up feeling like accidents.

What spoiled God's plan?
What forces keep trying to trap us
or control us?
Why do we try to be free of God
rather than free for God?

Cain, keep this in mind
and think about your own life for a while,
your own desire to play God,
and we'll continue our search tomorrow.

Conversation Two: ON WITH THE GAME

So "God" is the game, Cain?
Not the beginning,
but the game?
And we're all playing,
trying to master each other
trying to be big,
trying to be someone?

But is that the way it should be?
Is that the way it was planned?
Maybe God made us
to be real men
and not a bunch of second-class gods
fighting each other?

Let's grant that God gave men
the urge to rule the earth,
the impulse to be king,
the dream of mastering the universe,
the drive to represent God
and make the world spin with His power.

Let's grant that God gave man everything
except the nature of a god.

That was God's mistake?

Perhaps.
But if so, He's been suffering ever since.

But, then again,
perhaps it was also man's fault.
Ambition and power can be an asset
or a disaster.
Man has never been content
to stay in his place.
He takes God's good things
and uses them for his own selfish ends.
He wants to be in charge.
He wants to be the Creator.

All right, Cain.
So you were right.
Man does want to play God.
But does that mean God is the game?

Or is the game something we invent

to avoid facing God
and to free ourselves from God?

Yes, Cain, yes.
I play the same game sometimes,
and I feel the same urge
to rule my own way
and eliminate God.

You say it was just a figure of speech
to call the game "God"?
That you don't really think about God?
That you don't try to be God?
That you can get along without God?

Well, that could be the point.

We try to get rid of God
by ignoring Him.
We become so involved in other things
we suppress our feelings about God.
We take our life into our own hands
and forget to look back
and see where we stole it.

We try to be really independent,
self-sufficient men,
standing alone.

And that's it!

That's what?

That's the temptation to be like God,
knowing good and evil . . .
and power and glory.

Did I ever feel that desire?

I sure did.

I've discovered that the more selfish I am
the more I stand alone.
And the more I stand alone
the more I think about myself.
And the more I do that
the more I lose sight of who I am . . .
or who I can be.
Then I begin to feel
like a biological curiosity.

Man is not meant to be alone.
Monuments are!

You don't think I feel that?
You don't think my words are any more

than a preacher's way
of making us feel guilty?

That's not quite true.
You tried to master your mother.
I, too, have tried to control people,
but in a different way.

I'm a sometime actor and a ham.
I enjoy being on stage
and holding the audience in my hand.
I like that kind of power.

But then, when I'm offstage,
I want the same kind of power.
I search for opportunities
where I can be the center of the conversation,
where I can draw attention to myself,
where I can be popular
or powerful
or wanted.

I'm not usually conscious of playing.
But that's my game . . . our game.
In this game we treat our friends
like playing cards.
And the stakes are high.
The players can lose themselves in the game.
They become players
and not people . . .
finally they become cards
shuffled and dealt by the best player.

Then one day,
the self-sufficient modern man,
the best player in town,
wakes up
and discovers he is playing solitaire.

There is nothing we can do about it, you say?
No way to break up the game?

Why not try anyway?
I suppose the first step
is to admit we are playing a game called "God"
and that we can't break it up
by ourselves.

But perhaps there is a prior step—
to find out if men have always played the game
the way we do.

There's another writer in Genesis
who tells a story about Adam and Eve.

Sure, you've heard it.
But it's really not such a silly story.
It's a picture of the first man . . .
and every man.
It's the story of the first loser
. . . like you.

I said loser . . . not lover.

Will you let me explain the story
the way it is in Genesis
instead of snorting
about your weasel-faced Sunday school teacher?

The first man is on center stage.
Beside him stands the first woman.
The scene is a garden, long, long ago.
The snake is part of the scenery.
He comes out of the woodwork, as it were.
But he's only an animal.

No, he's not really the villain.
He is a means for man to see new possibilities.

He is like sex,
or money,
or political power,
or technical skill.
He is like the drugs
those guys offered you.
It all depends on how and why
you use these things.
The snake was part of God's good creation,
but the first man and woman
heard in the words of the snake
a chance for unlimited power.
The snake was the sign
of a hidden mystery,
the greatest of all happenings.

Maybe a talking snake is rather weird,
but the point of the story
is not the snake itself.
Listen to the conversation
between the snake and the woman
before you write the story off
as ridiculous.
It goes something like this:

"Did God say you can't eat from that tree?"
asked the snake.
"That's right,"
said the woman, defending her God,

"God said we can't eat from that tree
or touch it,
lest we die."
Foolish girl!
God said nothing about touching.
By adding that remark
God seemed to become a tyrant,
taking away man's freedom.

So the woman was ready to listen
when the snake challenged
the words of God and said:
"God knows as well as you and I
you won't really die, my dear.
For when you eat you'll be like God,
you'll be enlightened
and know as much as God knows."

That desire,
that temptation to know as much as God,
to experience the full range of power,
to become completely independent . . .
even of God . . .
that temptation is the same today.

What happens when we succumb?

If we stand alone we die.
Isolation means death.

God was right.
If man ate he would die.
Ever since then man has been committing suicide,
breaking away from life with God
and trying to make it alone.

That's death.

All roads lead to death, you think?
There's no way out?
We may as well die with power
than die as puppets?
There's no second chance?

Hold it!
Assume for the moment that God intended us
to be real men
proudly representing Him
and making the earth into something worthwhile.
Is God going to forget that dream of His?
Is God going to ignore His plan
just because we've perverted it?

I guess it depends

on what kind of person God happens to be.

We know what we are. Right?
Fools who keep breaking up with God,
busting up His plan
and trying to get rid of Him.

Yes,
we want to divorce God
because we can't live with Him
and do exactly as we please.

You're glad about the divorce?
You think marriages never really work
because your father's marriage failed?
You see husbands and wives as enemies
who should never have been married
in the first place?

Well, then, maybe God is the enemy
now that you have tried to divorce Him.
Maybe He's the one you're fighting
and trying to destroy.

You know, it seems to me
that we can see signs of
your divorce,
your fight with God,
your anger with God . . .
all around us.

Those signs were in the story.
The first couple hid themselves.
They were ashamed of their nakedness.
The man blamed the woman for their fate,
and the woman blamed the snake.

Signs of divorce were everywhere . . .
in the fear,
in the pain,
in the crawling snake,
in the dusty ground.

God was no longer a game
for the first man and woman.

He had become the enemy.

You like that, hey?
Now it's in the open.
If there is a God
He is the enemy—
a divorced, rejected enemy.

He is everyone's enemy, right?

No one has ever conquered Him?
All men have broken away from Him
and tried to be gods, right?
And every man has divorced himself
from God, right?

Wrong!

Well, at least it's not completely right.
There's a story about one man
who was tempted to be great,
to become a hero
and have the world follow him.
He could have mastered the world
with his power.
He could have broken with God,
and been mighty.
But he didn't.

Why? Who?

Don't laugh when I tell you.

His name was Jesus.

Just a minute.
Let me tell you about his temptation.
He could have used this power
to change stones into bread
and eliminate all hunger.
He could have jumped from the temple
and had the people scream with praise
as the angels carried him gently down to earth.
He could have ruled the earth
if he, in turn, had worshiped the devil.

You don't believe that story?

Well, one thing is clear.
Jesus was tempted to be famous,
to be a glorious king.
But he didn't use his special power
for his own glory.
Instead he permitted himself
to be captured,
to be mutilated,
and to be killed.

You don't want to talk about Jesus?
That kind of thinking makes no sense?

Maybe it doesn't.
So for now, let's go back
to the story of the first two people
and their enemy.

What happened to them?

Well, God didn't kill them.
They survived.
They were thrown out of the garden
... partly for their own good.

No, God didn't just want to be rid of them.
He wasn't just punishing them.
He wasn't just mad at them.

He didn't want to have them
eat of the tree of eternal life!
He didn't want to have
immortal rebels on His hands.

So God let them die a slow death
outside of His garden, you suggest,
instead of killing them in the garden?

That's one alternative.
But there's another.
Perhaps He wanted to give man another chance.
Perhaps He wanted man to survive.

Perhaps He didn't divorce man at all.
Perhaps God still loved man
and, in His concern for man,
offered him another way to live with Him
instead of being forever against Him.

Why not?
He didn't kill man.
He gave the first couple some clothes
and kept talking to them.
He didn't desert them.

Perhaps God still wanted man
to be His man on earth
and make something of himself.
Why not?

If God's first plan for man
was ruined by man's desires,
why bother with another plan?
Why not forget about man
and try another experiment?

Yes, why not?

Sorry. I don't know.
That's God for you.
He never gives up.

You want to escape from God?
You don't want that enemy

following you **any longer?**
You don't want to be part of any more
of His experiments with man?

I don't blame you.
Run. Run. Run.
That's what we all do
when we hear God coming
through the garden
or the streets
or the back of our brain
or the words of someone we know.

I run, too.
I say, thanks for my life, God;
but let me live it my way.
Just keep away from me, God.
No more of Your promises.
No more of Your dreams for man.
I am the rebel. You are the enemy.
Let's keep it that way.
Let me clutch what life I have
and escape in peace.

All right, Cain.
Let's try to escape.
Let's assume God is the enemy
and find a way to escape . . .
before we meet tomorrow.

Conversation Three: BEHIND THE MASK

Well, well, Cain.
You're not going to run after all?

Why?

Oh, because it's silly to run from God . . .
like running away from air?
And once you start running
you end up running away
from everyone
and everything?
Anyway, God is not the real problem?
He's an imaginary foe,
like the air?

So what do you plan to do, Cain?
To spin around and face the world?
To set up your defenses,
build your walls,
and protect yourself from the real enemies?

So it's no longer a game, Cain?
It's a battle, is it?
A fight to survive
with tactics?
A war of nerves
and hearts
and loves?
And weak people . . . like us?

That's it, you say?

I agree
that your relatives wore masks
to play their little games
and cover their soft selves.
I agree
that many people are loud
or violent
or sweet
or religious
to hide the painful sight they see
when they look inside themselves.
And I agree
that many of my own friends
lose themselves in parties,

ask for gentle pity,
or undermine the name of their colleagues
to boost their own sick egos.

Yes, I admit all that.
But is that any reason for you
to ape the crowd
and become a crab
with a hard shell
built to disguise a soft soul?

Can you reverse the process, Cain,
and trust someone else?
Can you put your faith in someone
and offer that person all your hopes,
all your fears,
all your petty feelings,
all that is you?
Can you trust, Cain?
Can you touch someone
and let someone touch your deepest corner?
Can you, Cain,
before your shell gets too hard
and comfortable?

No, of course not.
That's asking too much.
But why?

It doesn't work, you think?
You know?
Because people won't trust you in return?
Because they cannot feel your pain
no matter how hard they try . . .
they don't really want to listen,
or love what you are?
Because they'll laugh at you,
they'll betray your sick tears,
they'll forget you,
and they'll want to get rid of you
because your trust and your illness
will only remind them
of what they want to escape
in themselves?

So you won't try it again?
Because trusting someone else
leads to breaking down walls between people
and exposing people's puny faith,
their uncomfortable past,
the black holes
deep in their emotions?

What?
Using trust like that
is the dirtiest way to fight?
It leaves people betrayed
and defenseless?
It means suicide?

Yes, perhaps it can lead to suicide;
perhaps it has.
But is your suggestion any better?
You expect to establish a fortress
all around yourself
by using all the techniques of power,
popularity,
and self-assurance
you see in those who make the grade.

Those ways to win
will be your bright and shining armor
to keep yourself from being crushed
in the battering of people
one against another.

Well, that's what you think.
Let me remind you about your cousin.
Why did you beat into his face
and pound him with your fists
until he was white?
Why didn't you control your feelings?
Why?
Couldn't you?
Do you really believe
that you can harness all the urges
that swell inside your heart
and finally explode the mask you wear
before a waiting world?
Can you?

No, I'm not immune from those feelings, either.
Lusts and passions burn in me,
sometimes quietly and subtly,
but they are there . . .
and they have the strength to destroy me.

They can destroy you
unless you find a way to meet them.
Right now they are your masters.
You beat up your brother,
you fled,
you ran scared,
you tried to be tough,
but you failed.

What makes you think you can change now?
What makes you suppose
you can conquer any one of these emotions
now?

Because other people have?

Have they? Who?

People like your namesake?
Other people like Cain?
Never.
Look at that story again.
Cain is the big man,
the strong man,
like the hero.
Abel is nobody much,
nobody at all.
That's what their names mean.
But God loves Abel
even though he is nobody much . . .
and perhaps because he is nobody much.

Naturally enough, Cain becomes furious.
He cannot stand God's love,
God's favor on his brother.
He cannot control his envy.

"Watch your step," cried God,
"There's something like a demon
lurking near your door,
waiting to devour you.
Fight it or you'll die."

But Cain slaughtered his little brother
and saw the bleeding corpse at his feet,
saw a carcass of death,
saw the red flesh,
saw his own ugly death,
saw the flinching nerves,
the last quivers of life,
saw the bloody end,
the end. . . .

So you think it's morbid
and melodramatic
to dwell on death
as if it were your own?

All right, where is your brother, Cain?
Where?
God is asking you.

A dirty question?

I suppose so.
But death is a dirty business
and surviving is your big question.
You want to know how to live
in conflict with other people.
You want to be powerful
without being exposed for what you are.
You want to have life
without seeing blood on your hands,
blood on the ground,
bloody death.

Well, you can't.
Your brother is there on the ground.
He could just as well be you.
Why not?

You don't want to discuss dying?
He's not your brother anyway?
The Cain story is just a story?
You don't want to talk about that brother?

Why not?
You're not responsible?
Didn't you kill your own brother?
Or at least your cousin?
Or someone?

You didn't really kill him, you say?
Fine. He pulled through the ordeal.
But was that due to your goodness?
Did you want him to live?
No.
You wanted him out of the way.
For one very real moment
you hated him,
you didn't try to revive him,
you cursed him.
Didn't you?

It's all over and forgotten?
That's your verdict?

Far from it.
His screams will not die that quickly.
He's in your mind,
isn't he?
He's behind your mask,
behind your shell,
behind your wall,
behind anything you may find
to block his memory.
His voice will reach you.

You can't get rid of him, can you?

I know you aren't the first kid
who made that kind of mistake.
On the contrary,
the voices of the beaten,
the battered,
the hungry,
and the diseased
keep filtering through our walls.
In the slums
and on the battlefield
we hear the sobs
of bloated babies
and tearing bodies.
In every hole on earth where people live,
kids are screaming with Abel
and kids are running away like you.
Screaming kids
and running kids,
screaming kids
and running kids,
endlessly screaming
and running,
screaming
and running . . . to their graves.

And you, Cain,
there is one screaming face
that makes all of the screaming real
and personal for you.
You cannot escape the voice . . . ever.

"I'm not responsible for my brother.
I have to live my own life.
I don't have to keep him."

That's the cry of every running kid,
shouting those words as loud as he can
to drown the voice,
the screaming voice behind him.

You may be able to escape God.
You may be able to escape fear.
You may be able to escape disaster.
But somewhere,
one day,
you will meet a brother
who asks for breath
instead of blood,
who asks for you
instead of your words.

What then?

You will never escape your brother.

There are millions of kids, you say,
kids who long to suck your goodness,
use your kindness,
play on your sympathy,
take advantage of your love
. . . if you are fool enough to offer any?
They're selfish kids,
half brothers,
local bastards
who squash your soft heart?

Yes, I suppose every man
who is ever a brother
is taken for a sucker.

And I suppose it seems an impossible task
taking the responsibility
for the lives of brothers everywhere.
That's too much to take.
Yes, maybe it is.

But wherever you run, young man,
you'll meet more brothers,
genuine aching brothers,
men bleeding with loss and pain,
men ready for death.
Day after day
you'll meet more and more and more
bleeding brothers.

No, there is no out,
no exit,
no escape hatch.

Ready for some help, Cain?
No?
Going to keep running scared?

The Cain of the Bible story
screamed bloody murder
until God finally gave in
and offered Cain protection
from revenge.

Want that mark of Cain, Cain?
Do you?
Want the power to survive,
as a murderer and a fugitive?
Want Cain's mask, Cain?

Yes, you would!

Then you could take advantage
of the protection from above
to achieve some selfish end
without fear of getting bloody
along the way.

That mark of Cain
was never meant to be a substitute for life
or love with brothers on the earth.
It couldn't offer healing
for the bleeding people,
the running people,
the dying people,
spilling over the edges of the earth.

You want the protection of Cain
so that you can skip town?

Well, it won't help.

Why?
Because, in addition to the brother
whose voice already bothers you,
I intend to face you with another death,
another murder,
another brother.

Yes,
whether you like it or not.

Yes,
Jesus Christ,
the brother you would happily disown,
ignore,
and forget.

Take a good look.
at that Jewish brother of yours.

No masks with him,
no excuses,
no running,
no escape . . .
but a mirror.

He's the man
in whom you can see man,
the honest man within men,
the cursed man within men,
the suffering man within men,
the bleeding man within men,
the real man within men . . .
exposed now for us to see,
exposed by us,

exposed to feel,
to scream,
to die . . . like Abel.

Sure, it sounds ugly . . .
man fully uncovered.
No earth over him,
no clothing to disguise him.
Only him.
Pure man.
Pure brother.
Letting it happen for others to see
what he is
and what we are . . .
yes, what we are before him . . .
weak closed clams,
unable to trust anyone,
least of all him.

Yes, yes. We're back to that,
back to trust,
to that weakness you damned earlier.

But that weakness was his commitment,
his pact with God.
He would trust God all the way,
all the way to his slaughter.

Some trust?

Yes, some trust!
Committing himself to love men,
to suffer their curses,
to absorb their ills,
to soak up their wrongs,
and to stop, stop, stop
their endless evil
by taking it deep into himself
until it would dissipate
and finally die.

You don't like to hear me talk like that
with outright God-talk,
or Jesus-talk, at least?

Well, it's time.
You saw one bloody brother
and it's time you faced another.
You heard his scream
and it's been getting to you.
Well, it's time I said my word,
my scream about Jesus,
and left it ringing in your mind, too.

This word about that man
will be even more bothersome
than the scream of your other brothers.
Because this is the word of the true brother,
the word of *the* man,
a real man doing what you can never do,
following the way of trust,
the way of surrender,
the way of death,
the way of Abel . . .
and doing it because he loves men,
men like you . . . yes, you.

The way of Christ
is the way of bleeding,
the way of self-exposure,
the way of trust in love.
And the word of that man
is the whisper of a brother
who is very tired
and whose breathing is very heavy
and whose life has passed unnoticed . . .
a whisper to come and follow,
follow and suffer,
follow and bleed with him.

Ridiculous?
Of course.

Makes you nobody?
To be sure.

But what do you want to be?

You can become the brother of Christ,
a partner of his suffering,
a man who trusts brothers,
keeps brothers,
heals brothers,
and absorbs evil to soften its blow.

That kind of life as nobody
may be worth something,
something very real . . .
as someone.

If you have the guts . . .
or should I say the faith . . .
to let yourself be exposed
so that other men in pain
may find healing and hope . . .
if you do,
then you may become more than a mask,

more than a puppet,
more than a puny mind
trapped in a shell,
and torn by every drive
that wells up within you.

But once we open the door
we are vulnerable,
we are in for it,
we are likely to be hurt,
used,
injured, because we follow
the foolish way of Christ.
And for what?

Think about that.
God must be a fool
if He lets us all be slaughtered
to keep Jesus company in the grave.
Or is He?
How big a fool is God?
How much bigger fools are we
if we dare to take Christ as our hero,
our man,
our example,
without knowing just why he came
or why we are trusting him?

Try that for size
before we meet tomorrow.

Conversation Four: INTO THE WATER

I see, Cain.
So you think God is no fool . . .
but a weakling.

It seems to you
that He didn't finish His plan for men?
He didn't free the world from evil?
He didn't stop the avalanche of wrongs
that keep smothering men?
He didn't rescue men
from all the forces of destruction
inside and outside of men?

He wouldn't?

Or he couldn't?

All right, Cain;
so forces of death keep invading.
And we do face
more than fierce drives
that generate within us.
We do find ourselves trapped in a place
where one pressure after another
closes in upon us . . .
and tries to mold our wills,
our feelings,
and our opinions.

Do you think you can rise up
and resist these pressures,
these silent giants?
Do you, Cain?
Some of them are big bristling giants
and others are fuzzy little giants
who come as friendly gifts
and cute toys.
But they are giants . . .
who live with us.
They pull and push
and put us in traction.
These are the evil forces
in school systems,
political groups,
church groups,
"in" groups,

advertising and machines
... yes, machines,
economic machines,
human machines,
machines of every kind.

These are the giants
who want us to conform
to the pattern of living they set
... yes, set to their advantage.

There's no way to escape
... except suicide?

Jesus Christ, you say,
won't be any more effective
than any other human agency
in fighting all these pressures?

So we may as well surrender
to all the systems that control us
... and enjoy their protection.

But, Cain,
to surrender is to die,
to suffocate at their hands.
Similar pressures have been active
for longer than you can remember.
Before you were born
the magic machinery of evil
was moving into each new system
and forcing people to conform
to the wishes of the leaders
and to break the spirit of the weak.

From the first grip of the doctor's fingers
on your soft head,
to the latest complex network of computers
filing your statistics,
you have been surrounded
by a clamor of forces
that shuttle you around,
mold your plans,
change your mind,
limit your freedom,
and try to determine your fate.

It seems that none of us are truly independent people.
We are affected by the smallest pill we swallow
and the largest electronic brain we enter
as a number on a card.
At one time or another
we are seduced by the music we hear,

the people we like,
the clothes and company we enjoy,
the dreams of the advertising kings,
and the mistakes about God
we inherit from our fathers.

We are like putty
which is constantly molded
by a little pinch here
and a fingerprint there
until we dry in our crack
. . . die in our crack.

Cain,
can you ever expect to step back
and choose for yourself
what you will be,
where you will go,
what you will become
as a human being in your own right?
Can you ever be free
from the unseen grasp
of your environment
or your past?
Can you escape
the death of your individuality
or your free spirit?
Can you?

Oh, there'll be many clever answers
that promise you freedom
from all that haunts you
and hunts you.
Religious commercials (of one kind or another)
will dangle dreams before you,
ideals of soaring success,
images of exciting beauty,
portraits of the feminine,
the masculine,
and the beautiful.
Yes,
tempting packages of glory
will offer you an unreal world
of love,
mystery,
and power
which none can ever attain.

Of course, the dreams change their shape
and the goals differ
from one generation to the next.

The young today may take for granted
the cars,
credit cards,
travel,
and college education
for which their parents struggled
long and hard.
Youth longs for new worlds to taste,
fresh excitement,
bold causes,
and wild fads . . .
yes, even violent fads.

That's really not your cry?
You've changed your tune?
You want to swing with the times
and gain the confidence you need
to face whatever comes?

Well, the powers that sell answers,
or hope,
or dreams,
or confidence
will intensify around you,
and there will always be buyers
like us
who search for answers
outside of ourselves . . .
answers bigger than we are.

These public salesmen
feed on our needs
to boost their own power
over people
over life . . .
and perhaps over God . . .
whether they realize it or not.

Then all the answers are traps
that expose a deeper need?

Yes.

There's a vicious cycle
with one need feeding off another?

Yes.

There's a chain reaction of evil
from one person to the next
and one organization to the next?

Yes.

Forces around us

feed off the need within us?

Yes.

Forces of life (or rather of death)
that injure people daily
lurk in every corner of life?

Yes.

And there is no means
of stemming this tide of ugly powers,
this chaos?

Maybe and maybe not.

If we go back to the beginning,
we can find a similar dilemma
in the story of the Flood . . .
evils everywhere,
evils beyond control,
evils in heaven,
evils invading the earth,
evils in all men,
evils in nature,
evils in society.

And that great experiment of God,
in making a man
to rule His earth in love,
seemed a failure.
It was time to end the experiment
and begin anew.

According to the biblical story,
God plans to end the experiment
by making the punishment fit the crime.
He sends chaos.
He returns the polluted earth
to one enormous mass of churning waters.
He opens the ceiling of heaven
and allows the waters above
to explode on everything.
Man had set his course for disaster
by his evil choices.
Disaster was the necessary result.

That, no doubt, should have been the end.
That should have finished mankind.

But it didn't.
Why?
Why didn't God end it all?
Why doesn't God end it all
if he is God

and not some weakling
twinkling with the stars?
Why has He permitted
evil forces without number
to live without end?

Why?

The odd thing about God
is His weakness for human beings.
He does the unexpected . . . for them.

He steps "into the water" of the Flood
and gets wet . . . for them.
He selects one man,
a strange fellow called Noah,
who outlasts the destruction of the world
and survives that busted creation.

There he is,
a ridiculous figure,
bobbing around in that bizarre boat . . .
like the original yellow submarine.
He is the fool
who believed God loved him.

By grace,
by some strange kindness in God,
by the touch of a mystery . . .
by something . . .
he turns up safe and dry
after going through the flood waters.

Sure, it must feel funny,
wild,
unbelievable . . .
like the one man who survives a plane crash,
like the one boy
who escapes from a mine disaster,
like the last man on earth
after a nuclear holocaust?
No.
No. Not really.
But rather like the first man on earth,
the man with a chance
to begin all over again.

God, it is said,
reversed the plan of death
and gave man a new beginning,
the fresh air of a tomorrow,
the song of a future.

Man, it is written,
could rule again,
free to avoid the old mistakes.

The new man
was God's new risk . . . and hope.

It didn't work?
God failed again?

Well, man failed!

He was the same as before.
He had a new world
and a second chance
but he was the same within.
The earth had changed its face
but man set the same forces
of evil in motion.

So God modified His plans once more?
You're right.
Changing the world
by destroying the earth
simply doesn't work.
"I'm going to have to live with man
and work with man . . . the way he is,"
said God to Himself,
"This total destruction by flood
is out.
No more floods.
No more chaos.
No, sir."

Weakness?

Call it weakness, if you like.
Say God changes His mind, if you like.
But I like to believe
that in that big decision
and in that story of Noah
we can see a young God
reaching out to love man
the way he is,
despite the forces of evil,
despite God's own justice,
despite everything.

There it is:
God's love coming to the surface,
God free to change the scene
for the real good of man.
And Noah is the sign
of just that.

But the world is just as rotten now,
you think,
as it was before the Flood?
Nothing much has changed?
It seems that God has rescued man
to have him suffer greater ills
eternally. . . ?
Where's the love in that?
In letting dying men die on?
Hang on?
Linger on?

At least the Flood
was a clean and rapid mercy killing
compared with what we face today?

That's true, I guess,
until you pause along the road of history
and feel another day of death.

That's true,
until you see
the God who stepped into the Flood
step into the land of death
and bring another flood,
a flood of life.

That you can't believe?

Naturally.

Look at Jesus Christ again.
He's more than Noah was.

God stepped into water for Noah.
God stepped into flesh with Jesus.

He saw that man coudn't do it alone
so He joined us,
He became part of the human race,
He became man,
He became weak.

Impossible?

Why?

A foolish solution?

Why?
Because it makes Jesus some kind of oddity,
with nonhuman blood in him?

Far from it.
That man Jesus
was the man Adam was supposed to be.

He was all man,
real man,
true man.

Every force from within
he faced,
felt,
and fought.

Every power from without
he sensed,
suffered,
and smashed.

Yet he is a real man,
in every way.
That's the impossible claim
we accept.

The invitation to be King of the Jews,
the master miracle worker of all history,
the first fearless conqueror of space,
and time,
and matter,
he rejects as worthless and selfish.

He comes as a man,
feels as a man,
lives and dies as a man . . .
but never becomes trapped in the system,
never a party to evil,
never runs away,
never wears a mask.

Instead he cleans up the temple,
fights the corrupt leaders,
reaches the broken people,
touches the underdogs.

All this is too good to be true?
We can't do what he did
even if it is true?
We can't be what he was
even if his claim is true?

No,
I'm not suggesting that you can
change over-night
and do what Christ did.
I'm not offering some magic formula
that enables you
to be another Jesus.

But I am suggesting

that you listen to his claim
before you laugh at his answer.
He comes as the same man we met before.
He comes offering life . . .
not fun, but life . . .
not escape, but life . . .
not another mask, but life . . .
his life.

He claims to be the deliverer,
the one who fought every evil,
exposed their vulnerability,
and broke their power to imprison man
forever.

He claims to hold the life power
which can
and will
struggle with death
but never, never die.

How do we make contact with him?
How do we touch,
feel,
know,
reach him across the centuries?

By trusting, listening, and walking in the water.

Yes, I know you damned trust
as an impossible solution to life.
But this man asks you to trust him,
to believe he is the victor over evil,
despite what you see around you.

This man asks you to step into the water,
to pass through death
in the flood of baptism,
and to join the people who live through him.

He asks you to listen to his word
with all your senses open,
all your feelings open,
your mind open,
your soul open.

Wherever his words of life
are spoken . . .
mixed with water,
lived among people,
heard at meals,
tasted in bread and wine . . .
he is there among us

as the man who knows us,
as the man who fights with us,
as the real soul of free men forgiven.

He is there with his power,
the word that injects life.

Through that word he lives on
and brings life.

But he died?

Yes, he died.

He died young?

Yes, he died young.

The system . . .
the evil forces killed him?

Yes, they did.

He lost?

No, he won.

He did not conform to the evils around him.
He did not become part of the dreams
or the systems around him.
He fought them all . . . all that was wrong,
all that destroyed the spirit of man,
and the wholeness of man.

And because he fought them
he was finally destroyed by them.

He had to die.
He had exposed evil in all systems,
in every man and place.
He had opposed the biggest powers
and gotten away with it.

He was a threat to all men,
all masks,
all sellers of old solutions,
all evil.

And so upon him all forces congregated.
"Get him" was the cry.

But instead of meeting evil with evil,
wrong with wrong,
blood with blood,
or murder with murder . . .
yes,
instead of following the path of Cain,
the way of all other men

who keep the chain reaction of evil going,
he deliberately let evil crush him,
take its full toll,
break him,
spend itself on him,
destroy itself in him.

The wrongs
and sins that fall on him
are those of all men.
He takes them
to break death and evil for us.

Because those powers
did their worst on him
they have used their ultimate weapon,
they have sensed their own defeat,
they have lost their sting
and one day must die.

We then are free to fight,
to change the world,
to continue breaking evils
everywhere.

We can fight
because we can smell victory . . .
his and ours . . .
then and now.

Wherever evils are broken,
wherever change is happening to free men . . .
to give men life and hope . . .
wherever sin is destroyed and broken,
we meet the work of God in Christ
and we rejoice.

We survive . . .
no, we live . . . we have a plan again.
We are back at work
with the first plan
to rule the earth,
to control it for good and God.

You don't want to identify with a victim,
a ruined man,
even if he did die
to suggest another way to live.

He died?

We all die?

So what, you say?

There is one more radical act of God,
one more action that
is even more unexpected.

He not only steps into the water
into human flesh,
into life itself,
but into death,
into the grave,
into the earth
from which He first made man.

And from there He returns
with new life for men,
with the Jesus men buried,
with a life that cannot be destroyed by death,
a life that lives on,
a life with God that does not die
but ultimately destroys death
and all powers of death
or evil.

He steps forth
to declare the victory of His man,
His son Jesus Christ . . .
real,
full,
final.

By stepping into the water . . .
into the grave with this man Jesus . . .
you are given the power
and the promise
that all the forces of life that imprison us
need no longer enslave us.
We can follow with him
to become individuals
free to oppose wrong . . .
and see the new life
that is breaking forth in the world
wherever he is at work . . . now.

Where can we see that life
rising from the face of the earth?
Where?

In those people who know his freedom,
those who have become honest human beings with him,
and who give their life in his cause
to heal other people
torn from God
or broken
by the evils of society.

Each time we ourselves touch another life
with this love,
this word of victory,
this word of new life from God,
we learn more of what it means to be
a whole person . . . discovering life.

Christ in us . . . makes us whole.
Christ with us . . . makes us live.
Christ for us . . . makes us someone.

Yes, I suppose it sounds like church,
like a dreamer
who knows a mystery
and struggles like a child
to explain the life he knows.

Come back and laugh at me . . .
come back and tell me
if none of this makes sense to you . . .
come back before this week is over.

Conversation Five: DEEP AT THE CENTER

Good, Cain.
You've decided that listening to God
is not a solution but a struggle,
that trusting in Christ
is not an answer but an agony,
that looking for life in other people
is not so easy,
that finding life by talking about Christ
is not a snap . . .
not at all?

You don't want this kind of life
because it seems foolish as well as tough?
You don't want this kind of answer
because it's full of hidden questions?

You can't pin God down . . . with this method?

You can't manipulate God?

Right. But wait!

In your whole life, Cain,
there was little that was good,
little healing, or trust.
There was nothing you could remember
that might give you hope.
There was no center,
no life-giving experience.

Then,
when your cousin offered you life,
said "Hi,"
and wanted you back,
you ran away.
Again, you ran!

It's easy to run from the good . . .
even when we long for it.
It is hard to risk loving someone
because if we lose that person
we feel more empty than before.

We try to love . . . and we lose.

We try to help . . . and we fail.

We try to heal . . . and we get hurt.

So many people know nothing more
than a long series
of hollow disappointments . . . and unhappy friends.

They have experienced little of that hope
which has a center in Christ
and moves in a circle of love
around his life.

We need a chain reaction of faith in Christ
who broke the chain reaction of evil
and liberated life in us.

What's faith?

What's faith in Christ?

What's this special experience?

Well,
it's a risky business.
It's trusting Jesus Christ
as a person who knows us for what we are.
It's daring to believe
that he was the one man in history
through whom God ended death. . . .
It's the pain of saying "Yes"
to suffering
and forgiveness
and new beginnings with Christ.
It's affirming that Christ is alive
in his men,
in his word,
in his world . . . here and everywhere . . .
that he is changing everything there is
for God,
for good,
for joy,
for a tomorrow,
for a new creation of things . . .
despite what we see around us.

Faith is the torment of trusting Christ
and tasting life . . . all at the same time—
not pleasure but life itself . . .
not answers but life from God . . .
not comfort but cries of hope . . .
not God alone but God in the suffering Jesus Christ . . .
not heaven but HIM.

That experience of faith,
that living song,
is a haunting refrain
that someone, somewhere, gives to us

and plants in our brain.

Sounds like hell?

No. Hell is feeling nothing.

Faith is alive
when the whole person knows
and feels the struggle to love,
to forgive,
to accept . . . because of Christ.

To grow in faith
our circle of experience,
our faith,
needs to intersect with new circles,
with other men of faith
who have fought
and found life . . . with God.

Like who?

Like me?

Well, let's go back to Abraham,
the man of faith
at the end of those stories
that we've been using
in these discussions.

In Abraham
God initiates a new stage in His plan.
After all the agonies with Adam,
Cain,
Noah,
and Babel,
God set out on another course of action.

With Abraham
the real history of God's people begins.

He is God's first fool?
Sure!
Abraham lived in a great city called Ur
where he could enjoy
all the thrills
of rich culture and wild worship.
Temples were gay,
gods were exciting,
celebrations were colorful . . . in Ur.
Things happened in Ur.

Strangely,
amid the shouting and singing of that city
Abraham hears a voice within,

a sound that others do not hear,
a message from God . . .
or so he says.
He is driven by this urge
to leave home, family, and friends,
and live in Palestine,
that sad and shriveled land.
He risks his life for that voice
and that land.
He senses a strange promise
that God would somehow give him
Palestine to be his own. . . .
But more than that . . .
from there, old Abraham would gain
a multitude of children
and build a mighty nation. . . .
But more than that . . .
Abraham with all his sons
was now to be the source of blessing,
the power of life,
for lonely people everywhere
without the hope
of knowing God himself.

What's blessing?
Well, blessing is a loaded term
. . . like freedom.
It's power and life and forgiveness
and laughter
and skipping children,
all together.
It's like an injection of joy.
It's like adopting someone
and making them part of the circle
of love,
kind eyes,
strong hands,
and a future together.
It is like an electric current of forgiveness
that gradually changes one person after another
as they touch each other
with their hopes,
their pains,
their faith in Christ
who brings forgiveness from God himself.

Abraham was to be the catalyst for that blessing . . .
the lifegiver for his world.

Why Abraham?

What makes him special?
Why bring up that old man from the past?

Maybe he was a deluded fool?
Why listen to him
because he listened to a voice
about a lousy land?

I guess you are going to have to start
trusting again, Cain,
listening and trusting,
listening to my word
the way that Abraham listened to God.

What's worth listening to?
Why listen to Abraham?

It all has to do with a covenant,
a covenant crammed with promises.

How?

What?

God's covenant was God's action
of binding Himself to a plan,
or rather to a man,
to blundering Abraham.
He selects Abraham
and all his sons,
all who trust the God of Abraham.
He ties them to Himself like a robe.
They are His.
They are bound by love,
by promise,
and by His purpose . . .
especially His purpose.
He gives them individuality,
a sense of direction
and meaning.
He accepts them as they are
and makes them His men.
He forgives them
and offers them a future.
He welds them in love
and builds them a dream.

How was that dream fulfilled?

How were the promises kept?

Not with the gift of an eternal world empire.
Not with the mastery of earth
by political power,

by brilliant literary achievement,
by lasting peace among men—
no, not by bringing Paradise on earth.

Far from it.

He kept His word
in His own way . . . at His own time . . .
by His own unexpected twist of history.

He came with Jesus Christ . . .
an odd son of Abraham.

Yes, that man again.

He stepped into history
with His answer to that dream,
His promise of life for all men
and blessing for the universe.

He came with Jesus
who brought a life
that leaps out everywhere
and touches every man in every corner.
He came to be the center of the circle
. . . not a hazy hope,
but a center for us.
He came as a man
with whom we can identify.

You don't like that?
You don't like to come back
with the same solution
of Jesus Christ as the answer of God,
the voice of God,
echoing with a new pitch?

Sorry.
If you want to hear something more
than the sounds in the room,
the whisper of space,
the trickle of your own hurt,
the slow rhythm of your own death,
you will have to be ready to listen
to someone outside of you . . .
someone like me,
someone like that man Jesus Christ
spinning at the center of the circle of all life,
whether you hear him,
see him,
want him,
love him . . .
or not.

You'd rather listen
to someone else?

Wherever you go people
will whip you with words and sounds,
slash you with scenes and colors,
but they will often turn your eyes
and ears
and trust
inward to your own searching soul,
or off
into the blue realms of tomorrow
on the outside of the circle,
or to those mighty screens
where history flashes its pictures
of war
and mystery
and man at his best
or man at his worst.
You're not sure what that means?

I am asking you, Cain,
to face me as an ordinary man,
who is listening to your cries. . . .
Yes, Cain, listening . . .
and listening as well
to the word of God coming from . . .
from the center of the circle.
And I'm asking you
to admit with me
that we are lost,
that we break away from this circle. . . .
We have no place to go . . . no center. . . .
Yes, I'm asking you
to turn your head . . . let me help you . . .
to turn toward the center . . .
to acknowledge that there must be more
than just free-floating people on earth . . .
to listen to the meaning behind us . . .
the Meaning . . . the Word . . . . the Purpose . . .
there . . . at the center. . . .

You cannot hear or see anything
at the center of things?

Why?

Is it because
you listen only to yourself,
look at what you want to see,
find no clues around you

that there is life
that is larger than life . . .
that there is presence . . . yes, unseen presence . . .
mystery . . . feeling . . . around us?

No, that is not the final answer to life!
It's a beginning.

I am merely saying
that there is more to life
than meets the eye,
meets the ear,
meets the hand,
yes, than meets the mind.

There is something, some force in life,
that is bigger than both of us.
And I am saying
that I find that something
in someone, in Jesus Christ . . . at the center.

The presence of God
that is God
at the heart of things,
God getting to the point . . .
to the center . . .
that presence broke through . . .
through the surface . . .
into the open . . ..
and was seen . . .
was heard . . .
was handled in Jesus Christ.

Your experiences don't give you
any kind of assurance
that there is another source of life
than the heart you know . . .
or any other kind of life
than the struggle you know
to survive
and get the best of your brother?

Perhaps, that's true . . .
but then, perhaps, it's not.

We run . . . as I said before . . .
we run from the deeper life,
the deeper pull that draws us
to God . . . at the center.

In my word to you . . .
in the welcome of your cousin . . .
in the blundering efforts of your uncle . . .
in the weak ways

of men who know forgiveness as one power
from that core of all things . . .
in those people you have been drawn—
yes, invited—to turn to the life
at the center . . .
that never dies . . .
and keeps us bound.

You want something more spectacular. . . ?
Sorry.

You'll meet your Christ . . .
in the message of men like me . . .
whether those men
are speaking through the pages of Scripture
or across your table.
People,
real people,
with the same human agonies as yours,
have met
and lived
and celebrated
the very freedom that comes
from knowing that we are bound by God
in that circle.

These people impart hope . . .
come as Christ . . .
continue his work
of breaking the forces of evil
and building the lives in the circle,
reaching out to mend the broken ties,
broken relationships,
broken families,
broken faith . . .
so that men might never lose contact
with Life at the center.

As we do this
we begin to realize
that somehow
it was not really we ourselves,
but some drive within us
that led us to speak and trust . . .
some power,
some spirit given to us.

How does all of this,
this link-up with life,
this agony of turning to the center . . .
to Christ,
make us . . .

make us new persons
with a fresh sense of identity . . .
a sense of being whole persons
rather than half-human figures
playing a game . . . of dreams, or God?

Abraham became someone
worth something . . .
because he had God's assignment
to mediate life to men . . .
to be an ambassador of hope,
an agent of forgiveness.

When we follow Abraham . . .
or rather his son, Jesus Christ . . .
we become part of the ultimate cause,
the underlying plan of God,
the rule of God
initiated in Christ.
We become the very ambassadors
chosen to rule the earth with him,
for him . . .
to rule as he did
absorbing the evil
and making history
by healing the torn people,
by giving ourselves to bring good
into every area of human living
and working.

When we are accepted fully
as we are . . .
as worth something . . .
as valuable human persons . . .
as men and women to be loved . . .
and to love . . .
when we are fully accepted that way,
we know what it means . . .
gradually . . . and day by day . . .
to be persons
and not puppets.

I repeat . . .
when we acknowledge
that THE PERSON,
THE HUMAN BEING,
Jesus Christ . . . takes us,
gives us worth . . .
loves us in our skins,
loves us in our tears,
loves us in our games . . .

and makes us his,
brings us into the circle of life
that comes through his suffering,
and our suffering with each other . . .
then we know . . . slowly . . .
and with healthy pain . . .
that we are persons
who need not be puppets,
or pawns,
or anything else
than what God made us to be.

We can be new men,
new persons in Christ,
bound into the Christ circle
where living men find themselves
because he found them
with a love . . . bigger than any of us.

Is the circle really important,
you ask? Isn't it enough to know God?

The circle is important
because the center . . . the Christ power . . .
makes the circle important,
makes everyone in that circle important . . .
special,
worth his death.

For in that circle of special people
we need not . . .
I said need not . . . stand alone.
We know there are others in that circle
who can hear our screams,
no matter how sour we have turned,
others with whom we can be honest . . .
who will be Jesus Christ to us . . .
and hear us for him . . .
forgive us for him . . .
accept us for him.

We, in turn, need to trust them,
as we would that Christ.
We, in turn, need to treat them
as worthy of love . . .
of risking our feelings,
risking our inner selves,
risking our trust to give them the life
we have tasted from others.

To trust someone

is to treat that person as a true person,
as human.
It is to honor him
It means he becomes special . . .
accepted . . .
drawn into the circle of new life.

What else happens in that circle?

Many things.

Forgiveness, for example,
the life-word of the circle,
the expression of love from Christ.

No, forgiveness is not merely a word,
not merely saying, "I'm sorry,"
"Forget it."
Far from it.
Forgiveness is the process
initiated by God to heal the broken world,
to bring it back to Him through Jesus Christ.
And that process of announcing life
and sharing life
by forgiveness, by accepting,
by being open persons to others . . .
that process goes on.

It moves back and forth
between the people in the circle,
the family circle,
the church circle . . .
in every circle
that looks to Christ
as the one who brought us all back to God,
reconciled the world to God,
loved the world . . . to give it life.

In this chain reaction of forgiveness,
love,
person to person listening,
man to man struggle for life . . .
whatever you call it . . .
in this process Christ is alive.
In this work we continue the struggle
against evil,
against any process,
any system from without
that would make us less than men,
less than human,
less than individuals
worthy of the name

because Christ has given us his name
and affirmed our worth.

Thus the plan of God for man,
once expressed at the beginning of time,
is working itself out.
We are part of that plan.
We know the victory will be ours,
the freedom ours,
the rule of earth in love . . .
because Christ,
as one of us,
accomplished that for us.

No, you will not be able
to escape completely
from the pressures around you
that threaten to make you a punch card.
But you can be free
from their ultimate power to destroy you.
You can be part of the campaign
to destroy them.
You can face them for what they are . . .
exposed by Christ . . .
as forces of evil and death
destined to die.

No, you will not escape completely
from the feelings within you,
the urges of your deepest being
which seem to control you
or make you a weakling behind a mask.

But you can be free
from their ultimate power to destroy you.
You can be part of a deep struggle,
with the power of Christ
and the healing hands of men,
to expose those inner hostilities,
to face them,
to see them as potential evils
that Christ has met and mastered
so that they may be overcome in your life.

Yes, forgiveness
is that continuing struggle,
with the love of Christ,
to forgive others
by struggling through *their* oppressions
with them,
and to accept forgiveness
from others

by struggling through *your* doubts
and oppressions
with them.

I didn't say it was easy.

I didn't say there was a miracle
at my finger tips
that would solve everything.

But then again,
there is a miracle . . .
that we talk of what happens
deep inside us,
deep in the world,
deep at the center of the circle of life.

This is a miracle
that points to the deepest miracle of life itself . . .
new life,
new hope,
rich signs of joy . . .
the miracle of Jesus' resurrection.

That is the last straw, I know.

But that is the last word,
the impossible word,
the one word
that says life without end,
unlimited life at the center
for all in that circle.

Because of that life together
we are brothers,
circle brothers,
soul brothers,
life brothers . . .
yes, my brother Cain . . .
persons worthy of the name,
worthy of the love,
worthy of the life,
worthy of the plan of God . . .
made worthy by Christ our brother
deep at the center of all life,
deep within us,
deep in his words,
deep between us.
And all of that
reveals God to be God
and not a game.

Where are you going, Cain?

Are you leaving?

Are you going to wander again?

Cain,
my brother,
may I walk with you
until this night is over?

I have been that way before.

P.S. You may know Cain or me
    because you have lived through our turmoil
    in your soul.
    I only wish I knew you.
    Perhaps I do?